BRITAIN IN PICTURES
THE BRITISH PEOPLE IN PICTURES

WILD FLOWERS IN BRITAIN

GENERAL EDITOR
W. J. TURNER

The Editor is most grateful to all those who have
so kindly helped in the selection of illustrations,
especially to officials of the various public
Museums, Libraries and Galleries, and
to all others who have generously
allowed pictures and MSS.
to be reproduced.

WILD FLOWERS
IN BRITAIN

GEOFFREY GRIGSON

WITH
12 PLATES IN COLOUR
AND
22 ILLUSTRATIONS IN
BLACK AND WHITE

WILLIAM COLLINS OF LONDON
MCMXXXXIV

PRODUCED BY
ADPRINT LIMITED LONDON

PRINTED IN GREAT BRITAIN BY
WM. COLLINS SONS AND CO. LTD. GLASGOW
ON MELLOTEX BOOK PAPER MADE BY
TULLIS RUSSELL & CO. LTD. MARKINCH. SCOTLAND

LIST OF ILLUSTRATIONS

PLATES IN COLOUR

Rich is thy soil, and merciful thy clime ;
Thy streams unfailing in the summer's drought ;
Unmatch'd thy guardian-oaks ; thy valleys float
With golden waves : and on thy mountains flocks
Bleat numberless ; while, roving round their sides,
Bellow the blackening herds in lusty droves.
Beneath, thy meadows glow, and rise unquelled
Against the mower's scythe. On every hand
Thy villas shine . . .

JAMES THOMSON : from *Summer*

THE FLOWERS WE HAVE

VERY few flowering plants are only found in the British Isles. So it is not wise to be national—or too national—about English flowers. You may find an ordinary white dead nettle more at home in a damp wood in Siberia than by a village road in Somerset or Kent. We are part of Europe, separated in geologically recent times, and divided from Europe only by a shallow sea. At its narrowest, we are within sight of the European cliffs. Our flowers occur on the other side of that shallow sea, and, many of them, far back beyond Europe into Asia, and even to America. Marsh marigold, for instance, ranges "throughout Europe and temperate Asia to North India and North America," according to Bentham and Hooker's *British Flora.* Ivy is "common in Western and Southern Europe, Northern Africa, the Himalaya and in Japan." Nettle, the ordinary nettle, stings "throughout Europe and Russian Asia, from the Mediterranean to the Arctic regions," and has been "carried as a weed to other parts of the globe." Or, to pick on another, more handsome flower, sea pink grows, not only in Britain, but "on muddy or sandy sea shores, and on maritime rocks, in the northern hemisphere, from the Arctic regions to near the tropics." It appears again in the southern hemisphere beyond the tropics, "and also at considerable elevations in the high mountain-chains of Europe and Asia." To discipline our pride, various writers have emphasised that, on the whole, British plants are only a fragment of the European flora. So perhaps it would be better to talk, not about "British Wild Flowers," but about "Wild Flowers in Britain."

All the same, our impoverished fragment does well for itself. It is impoverished in the number of kinds, not in the richness, abundance, and colour of flowers. The climate and the shape and the surface of the British Isles are favourable, on the whole, to the plants we have. We have plants which are out in most of the twelve months of every year, and a distribution of different colour from early spring to autumn, which I fancy

7

is not, at any rate, excelled in Europe. First of all we have to thank a sea climate. It is difficult for us, or for a plant to get fifty miles away from the sea. In winter we have warm winds blowing in from the Atlantic, west and south-west—winds that often allow primroses to be out in the western counties on New Year's Day. Some parts are colder, some drier than others, but, on the whole, we have a mild and moist country. Plenty of rain ; little extreme, enduring cold ; little extreme, enduring heat.

"Misty-moisty was the morning
Damp was the weather . . ."

Going to Northern Europe in April, or, say, to Dalmatia in July, shows the advantage of being mild, and moist, and average. In April, in Northern Europe, the soil still too cold, and the frost still too cutting, for plants to begin their job ; in Dalmatia, on the edge of the sea in July under the limestone mountain wall, all the fine flush and fancy of the spring flowers dried up into seed and brownness. If we have sheets of primroses down over a Cornish hillside, if we have an acre or two of foxgloves down from a cliff-fort almost to the sea in Pembrokeshire, if we have a hollow in the chalk downs in Wiltshire made purple with field geranium, or if we cool our eyes with a splash of the clearest chrome yellow monkey-flower in a stream, or with water-meadows green even at midsummer, we have to thank this reasonable climate of ours.

Climate is more important than soil. The worst soil will soon get a colony of flowers, and, if the climate allows, will in time become modified and enriched. If a bomb blows a house off its foundations, the ruins will soon enough be colonised by something, rosebay willow-herb or groundsel. Or if the cellars are cleared of debris, before long a few curving stems and yellow flowers of coltsfoot will be coming up and out, even in Central London. Difference of soil and difference of underlying rock or sand or clay we have plenty of in Great Britain, but on the whole it is more important to flowering plants to have geological formations which mean a mixed, uneven surface, and a variety of the right shelter and the right homes. English landscape offers plenty of shelter from wind, plenty of corners, and cliffs, and sand dunes, plenty of damp hollows, plenty of streams, and plenty of sun-traps. I think of two parishes. First, one in Cornwall, of 4,000 acres. It has got at least a dozen streams, several oak woods, bits of heathland, the shelter every so often of deep valleys and tall earth hedges, outcrops of rock, and so on. With a mild moistness of climate, the ungrazed and unploughed parts of those 4,000 acres make a perfect natural garden. Plants liven up the waste ground, the woods, and hedges, and corners, and marshes of the parish—gorse, broom, prim-roses, wood anemones and blue bells ; stitchwort and purple orchis in the spring hedges ; great later growths of hemp agrimony ; yellow sticky-stemmed bartsia in the meadows, pennywort on the walls and rock, hollow

8

HONEYSUCKLE

Drawn and engraved by William Kilburn 1745–1818

From Curtis's *Flora Londinensis*, 1777

By courtesy of the Director, Royal Botanic Gardens, Kew

ORPINE

Coloured engraving from Curtis's *Flora Londinensis*, 1777

By courtesy of the Victoria & Albert Museum

hogweed filling up the damp gardens, monkey-flower around mill-wheels, purple loose-strife, and so on ; and a sprinkling of rarer plants, such as soapwort and alkanet, and the delicious striped geranium of Southern Europe, *Geranium versicolor*. The Wiltshire parish is not so rich or favoured. But it runs on either side of a long chalk escarpment. Up on top, chalk downs and downland plants. On the cliff itself, harebells and restharrow. Then, sheltered from the north and east winds, damp woods under the slope, with blue bells, wood anemones, and Herb Paris, and ramsons, the white, starry garlic, which covers a wood's floor delightfully, but has never been able to get much of a place in human sentiment. Then, down below the woods and the bramble-clumped and ragwort-spotted talus of the cliff, wide clay meadows with hemp agrimony and willow-herb in the ditches, water-holes with pond-weed, water crowfoot, and brooklime, and everything in the meadows themselves from the first crop of dande-lions, following the sun round, to the summer mixture of daisies and meadowsweet and the mahogany, hard, curious heads of the greater burnet.

A rock, a wall, a valley, a hollow, well placed, creates its own specially favourable conditions. Side-valleys come down to join the big Tamar Valley between Devonshire and Cornwall. These side-valleys run just the right way and are so deep and steep that they have the still airlessness of a hothouse ; they catch and hold the sun, and grow on the chocolate of their slopes some of the earliest and best strawberries and lettuces and flowers in England. Or think of the limestone scars of Yorkshire, under-neath Ingleborough, for instance. The wind cuts across these grey, level tables of rock, but down in the joints and pockets of the rock, grows a luxury of flowers and fern. Two feet down, in half-shade and damp, well out of the wind, the rock shelter creates little pockets of woodland flora, bluebells, wood anemones, sanicle, dog's mercury, spleenwort, hart's-tongue, wood-sorrel, lilies-of-the-valley even (though those also grow on the table itself). Our average, ordinary landscape gives plenty of protection to flowers, and, like the climate, does not go to extremes. We haven't vast areas of marsh, or dry, stony upland, we haven't vast mountain ranges of great height, or huge monotonous forests. We enjoy an average of everything and this takes good care of our 'fragment' of the flowers of Europe. It may be a fragment, but remember that it is con-tained within a fragment, contained in a small, crowded land area, in which variations of a mild climate and diversities of soil allow the plants to vary from alpine types in the north, or in Scotland and in Wales, to types, only a few hundred miles away, or less, which belong to the warm Mediterranean or the coasts of Portugal.

I ought to add figures explaining the fragment. According to Claridge Druce, there were in 1931—including sedges and grasses and ferns and plants of some genera such as the hawkweeds and brambles many species in which do not differ conspicuously from each other—there were in all 2,270 native kinds of plant (the figure for France is 4,300) ; 106 plants which had come in from abroad and naturalised themselves ; 293 aliens which seemed pretty well established and 1,799 foreigners from Europe, Asia, Africa, America, Australia, etc., which occurred, but probably would not settle. That is to say, 4,468 species. And of these, 60 are trees which grow more than thirty feet high, 380 are shrubs (this includes 180 of the more or less similar brambles), and seven are climbing shrubs.

I wonder if most people could write down the names of thirty wild flowers which they know by sight ?

LOVELY, ORDINARY, STRANGE

IF we pass beyond the limits of twenty or thirty, we begin to pick and choose, to anthologise among flowers, for several reasons. I find I like some plants because they are rare, some because they are peculiar, some because they combine an exceptional loveliness of colour and form. All, or some, of the reasons may be combined. And the loveliness of a plant is not always an individual loveliness, but a loveliness of a few, or many, plants of the same kind growing together in their natural scene. The single plant illustrated on a page in a flower book is an ideal abstraction, and partly a surviving habit from the older days when the expert's job was only to find plants, and divide them up into orders, families, genera and species. We cannot, emotionally, separate a flower from the place, or the conditions, we usually find it in.

Only a few plants, all the same, are part of the common language of English emotions. The daffodil, or the primrose, or the ivy, or the yew tree, for example. And they are not always the most beautiful. Daffodils, in their right place, are captivating enough—straggling up a slope and just showing their heads in a tangle of brambles and grass, or under the trees and between the rocks along the bank of a stream. But analyse a daffodil, and it turns out to be a flower that owes as much to the daffodil tradition and to its way of appearing early in the spring and in mass, as it does to its own beauty. Many excellent plants which come out at a crowded time of the year have hardly even the small recognition of a common name.

I am not sure, either, that primroses deserve, in themselves, all the honour they are given. The primrose smells of a new year, its leaves have an endearing crimple, but taken as an individual, it cannot really claim exceptional loveliness of form or colour. It is a plant homely and ordinary in detail beside a yellow-centred, elegant stitchwort. The way it grows, its relation to the ground, to the brown debris of a previous year, its scattered abundance, its earliness, its candour and eye-openness, are its virtues.

Menyanthes trifoliata. Common Buckbean. 2.

BOGBEAN
Coloured engraving from Baxter's *British Flowering Plants,* 1837

We should be all for every possible mixture of virtue in any plant. The formal beauty of an individual specimen is only the first requirement. Ruskin, who is responsible for a good many of our likings to-day and our notions of preserving ancient buildings and protecting rural England, wanted in flowers this placing of the leaves, and flower, and bud, and stem, combined with pure colour and rich surface, and still further associated with moral lessons. He did not approve of peculiarity, or believe "in his very heart," as Samuel Palmer did, "that all the very finest original pictures, and the topping things in nature, have a certain quaintness by which they partly affect us ; not the quaintness of bungling—the queer doings of a common thought ; but a curiousness in their beauty, a salt on their tails, by which the imagination catches hold on them." I prefer Palmer's view. I would take Ruskin's belief that "the flower exists for its own sake —not for the fruit's sake . . . the flower is the end of the seed—not the seed of the flower." But no flower need be admired simply for its loveliness, or for the traditional feeling about it. It is human to prefer what is interesting in appearance, in behaviour, and in history. It is human to make symbols out of dry ground or clear water, and all to do with them. If Professor Salisbury tells me that some of the southern rarer species came into England possibly with the Megalith builders or if Clement Reid provides evidence that fumitory—Erdrauch, earth-smoke, to the Germans—which is anyway one of the loveliest of plants, came in with the Neolithic farmers about 4000 B.C., then I find fumitory, and those southern flowers, all the more attractive. Ruskin was very much repelled by ideas, still fresh in his life-time, about the relation of colour in flowers to insects and natural selection. It didn't allow the flowers to be the end of the seed (a fiction, if you like, but one that every botanist accepts in his own flower garden). All the same, the attraction of any plant is increased, and ought to be increased, by any curious fact about it. To the sentimental, or the Anne Pratt, or the quotation fact, I prefer facts about history and distribution and adaptability, the facts of the plant itself. Nettles are more interesting to me because they like the nitrogen of decay, and because they can sting. When the Linnaean collections were being photographed at the beginning of the war, the photographer was stung by a nettle which Linnaeus had dried two hundred years ago. I like a particular frail catchfly, which occurs in several English counties, because it is lovely, yes—and also because the purple spot on each one of its five white petals seemed to Linnaeus like one of the five wounds of Christ. So it was called *Silene quinquevulnera*. But I'm afraid that is a reason outside the plant. Bogbean I like for the lacy exquisiteness of its white beauty and pink buds rising out of black bog water, and also because I know it to be an ancient hardy plant which was here before the Ice Ages, and which grows in the Arctic, in Greenland, and Iceland, as well as alongside the snipe's nest which I found one year in Pembrokeshire. Forget-me-not I think of not only beside a slow river like the Mole or the Cherwell, but rooted in slime, just below the point where a hot spring trickled out of a black volcanic slag heap, and steamed up into the cold of the Icelandic air, opening its eyes like the blue flower of Novalis. And so on.

GROUP FROM THE FORGET–ME–NOT FAMILY
From left to right : Evergreen Alkanet, Tuberous-Rooted Comfrey
Lungwort, Jacob's Ladder, Borage, Gromwell, Houndstongue, Bugloss
Coloured engraving from Loudon's *British Wild Flowers,* 1846
By courtesy of the Royal Horticultural Society

VIPER'S BUGLOSS

Coloured engraving after a drawing by James Sowerby 1756–1822

From Sowerby's *English Botany*

A poor, *exclusive* reason for liking a plant is certainly because it splashes a big area with its own uniform colour; and in this way, in the last hundred years or so, several plants have pushed themselves into an emotional prominence that I do not think they deserve. Heather and bluebell, for example. I doubt if a wide area of purple was much felt to be beautiful before 1850 or 1860.

After all this, I may not now seem so perverse if I say that a woodland plant I would prefer is the curiously named, curiously shaped Herb Paris. If we can talk of "English" plants, then Herb Paris (which I first saw in a wood in Normandy) has an English individuality. I know it every year in small patches, on mossy ground under hazels and oak trees, in a Wiltshire wood, ten or eight plants to a patch. There is no other plant at all like it in England. It is a surprise, and an elegant oddity, with its flower stem curving up from the centre of its four regular leaves, its yellow thin petals showing off its big, black ovary, which turns into a blacker and bigger berry. "One Berry" is the name it was first recorded by in 1548.

Herb Paris embodies much of what I look for in a wild flower. It has a range from the Mediterranean to the Arctic, and into Asia. It is not, with us, too pushing, or too rare, too much talked about, or too remote from an individual appeal to one's own feelings. So it comes high in a list of the good plants to look for every year, in which I include fritillary, wood anemone, sainfoin, restharrow, Cornish moneywort, bugle, woodruff, bogbean, deadly nightshade, henbane, greater celandine, viper's bugloss, orpine and musk mallow, mistletoe, and an isolated spindle tree, standing free, away from a hedge, in fruit.

FRITILLARIES, NIGHTSHADE, AND OTHERS

THE best time of day to go and see a field of fritillaries in April is not long before sunset, or not long after sunrise. For all their dark, checkered maroon, fritillary petals are thin and show the sunlight through, when it levels down across a Thames water-meadow. To see them like this, is to get the last refinement out of their elegance and individuality, their grace, their snakiness, their blend of pink and plum-purple.

There is always complaint about picking fritillaries, but as it happens, I think it is necessary to see them in low sunlight *and* to pick them, or a few of them, to get their full beauty. It is a flower that needs to be seen, first of all in the mass, then as an individual, so that it gives up what Gerald Hopkins called a flower's "inscape." The beetle gets the best view, and since we are not beetles, we pick flowers and put them more on a level with our eyes. No amount of scolding will prevent people from picking fritillaries or prevent gypsies (they are very appropriate to

Fritillaria Meleagris

FRITILLARY
Coloured engraving from Curtis's *Flora Londinensis*

gypsies) from selling them at term time in the streets of Oxford. They are far too odd and reach far too high a beauty. Anyone living in the North or West, outside the fritillary counties, should walk at least once in a fritillary field before he dies.

Henbane and deadly nightshade live near each other in flower books as members of a large family which includes tobacco and potatoes. They are both poisonous, and one gets into the habit of thinking of them together. But they like different places; henbane, viscid and downy to the fingers, is the exquisite, clammy emanation of waste ground and sunshine, nightshade the emanation of evil in dark corners. I knew deadly nightshade first in chalky angles of the Mickleham Downs in Surrey, but the image I carry of it is tall plants by gravestones in an abandoned chapel yard under an old quarry, not far east of Bristol—a dissenting chapel yard. Linnaeus named it after Atropos, and it is a very suitable plant for one of the Fates, determined and strong, wide leaves, gloomy brown flowers, producing black and shining berries.

There are two other good plants in that quarry, gromwell, and one plant I ought to have included in my first list of good things—stinking hellebore. I admit that I shifted one small plant of hellebore to a gully in my own garden, into a rather similar habitat under the chalk escarpment I have already mentioned; and there it does well, and towers up from its very dark, leathery divided leaves, to its flower-head, light and lively as a pale green flame. It is a fine thing to see it flaming away early in the

14

year with snow all around. Bract, then flower-stem, then sepals, are all of this same green, except that, inside and out, some of the sepals are usually tipped with a rich purple. Snails help to distribute the seeds of this hellebore. Behind the seeds, and attached to them when they fall, there is a white, fleshy band, which attracts snails (and ants as well). This is the oil-body, or "elaiosome." The snail eats it for the oil, the seeds stick to the snail by its slime, and so get scattered at a snail's pace. As good a fact, nearly, as the fertilisation of aspidistras by slugs.

Henbane, perhaps, ought to go with some of the plants I shall describe which, as seed, enter casually from Europe. It comes up by hen-runs as though seeded from poultry food ; and it very easily disappears. Along my chalk cliff in Wiltshire there is a small platform of level turf outside a farm-house, and there henbane has grown for a great many years. Hen-houses stand alongside, and the soil is not chalky, but a patch of green-sand from under the cliff. Last year I took someone to see the henbane. It had gone. Henbane is said to be decreasing like that all over England. It is an annual, and a plant much more at ease on the waste heaps, say,

COLTSFOOT
Coloured engraving from Curtis's *Flora Londinensis*, 1777-1798

of the French Riviera. A bad English summer could no doubt prevent the seeds from ripening.

There are many good points about henbane, and careful judges have liked it. Crabbe had a taste for its "pencil'd flower of sickly scent," which decorated his East Anglian borough, and W. H. Hudson put it nearest the fritillary for coupling strangeness and beauty, in its "exceedingly dark purple centre and petals a pale clouded amber yellow, delicately veined with purple brown." His delineation is worth comparing with the insensitive and not so accurate description of the professionals, Bentham and Hooker : "corolla above an inch long, pale, dingy-yellow, with purplish veins." Another more popular flower book says "flowers dirty yellow and purple."

To talk of a commoner plant, I do not know that many people have had much to say of bugle ; but it has a distinguished and rather brisk way of growing in patches where it is shady and damp, and it has a blue peculiar to its flowers—while they are still in bud—a leaden, sullen blue, which extends into the leaves. Its full blue is brilliant and shown off by this leaf darkness. Gerald Hopkins noticed it and liked it, and used bugle as an adjective of colour.

Greater celandine has a good history and physique. It is one of the first flowers you meet on getting near to a village. Its grace, the clear yellow of its flowers (compare the hard sulphur of charlock), and its blue green leaves, made it appeal to Dürer, so it is one of the few plants which have had their likenesses perfectly drawn. Break the stem, and out comes a drop of juice, vividly yellow, or, rather, orange. (I once used to anoint a wart with it, according to the flower books, but beyond imparting a yellow stain, it never had the slightest effect on the wart viruses.) Celandine is held to be a plant introduced, or reintroduced, into this country, by the Romans. It certainly seems to depend for its continuance on being associated with man. It grows where the clearing of ditches and trimming of hedges prevent too severe a competition. Its seeds also have an oil-body, so it gets many of them scattered for it by ants.

Switching into full summer, consider the splendid handsomeness of viper's bugloss and of sainfoin, which both belong to dryness and sun. Bugloss is vipery all right, combining a roughness of stiff hairs and a deep blue abundance of close-set flowers, which start off pinkish purple. I think of it as a kind of English cactus, and indeed saw it first, as a child, when I had only admired it in coloured plates, in a clearing of oak coppice on a hillside, a scrubland with a very large population of adders. It is a successful plant, fairly abundant, liking a shingle bar out of reach of the tide as much as a chalk-pit or chalk downs. Bugloss is prickly heat. Sainfoin is pure heat, an Impressionist plant in a pink striped dress, individual, and very often a forage escape. Next to seeing and smelling a field of black-spotted beans may be reckoned the sight of a field of sainfoin

HENBANE
Engraving after S. Curtis, from Curtis's *Botanical Magazine,* 1823

under a blue sky, like a drove of ladies by Manet. Persia and Morocco
are some of the places where it grows ; and it occurs in hot summer
descriptions in novels and stories by Maupassant.

Cornish moneywort (*Sibthorpia Europaea*) I take to be a name made up
by the botanists. It creeps inconspicuously along in the damp in Cornwall
and Devon, and south Somerset, in the south of Wales, and in Kerry, in
Portugal and Spain, and elsewhere ; and it belongs to an assembly of
plants which have been much argued about—the plants which only grow

17

in Britain in the milder, moister, and warmer South-West. Not much of a plant, but its tiny size and its tiniest pink spots of flower, give it the attraction of miniatures, like a Bible the size of a penny stamp.

Mistletoe—its berry is the glazed, milky eye of death, a white thing to be added to the terrible chapter on whiteness in Melville's *Moby Dick*. Orpine is another matter. I once saw it in a deserted orchard in a damp coombe, on a day when the sycamore stems were glistening with rain. A large adder shining in coils lay underneath the flesh of its stems and leaves.

It was like the colophon of a mediaeval book, the tree of life and the snake. Orpine, for me, is a genuine symbol of life. It has other names, "Midsummer Men" (plural, because each plant has several flowering stems, each with its own corymb of flowers), and "Live Long," and "Life Everlasting." Often grown in cottage gardens, it stays on when the cob walls of the cottage have been washed away to the ground and the last apple tree has rotted out. Its flowers mix magenta and purple, and they look well and deliberate in the long grass of an earthen hedge. There are several other fine plants which go on marking an old settlement, say, a group of houses which have no existence now except on a mid-nineteenth century map. Half a dozen of them are balm, with lemon-scented leaves, periwinkle, soapwort, gooseberry, monkshood, and the Arabic named alkanet with its white-eyed gentian blue flowers among leaves which are healthily dark green. I come across orpine sometimes at points of happiness or importance in my own life. It comes suddenly, and alone, and striking, with not much of its colour all at once.

Napoleon had orpine growing at St. Helena, because it was good against cancer, he believed.

RARITY

TO find what is rare is the last pleasure left to millionaires. A flea to Lord Rothschild, to add to his collection of fleas (someone I know gave him an Anglo-Saxon flea from the clothes of an Anglo-Saxon interment), was no doubt as much as a Velasquez, and, I should expect, even more than a Velasquez, to Pierpont Morgan. And a rare plant gives at any rate a more durable delight than a glimpse of a rare bird. A rare plant stays put. A rare perennial, like the pinks of the Cheddar Gorge, or the peony on the island of Steepholm, or the bloody crane's bill below Ingleborough can be visited again and again ; and there are many now classic sites where a plant has been admired in its rarity for more than two hundred years. It is like the artist going to see Gordale Scar, visited by Gray in the autumn of 1769, painted and splendidly

Fumaria officinalis

COMMON FUMITORY
Coloured engraving from Curtis's *Flora Londinensis*, 1777-1798

exaggerated more than forty years later by the powerful Romantic, James Ward, revisited and, I suppose carefully, recorded by the painter Inchbold for the Pre-Raphaelites, and interpreted again for ourselves by John Piper in 1942.

The Cheddar pink has been known on the Cheddar cliffs since 1696. A succession of botanists have been to visit rare plants at Bristol, such as the Bristol rock cress (*Arabis stricta*), which was picked around the gorge by Ray in 1686, and by Sir Joseph Banks in 1774, and is still there flowering in April and May. The bloody crane's bill I just mentioned grew on Ingleborough in 1666, when it was recorded in Christopher Merritt's *Pinax Rerum Naturalium Britannicarum.* I saw it there this summer still flaunting its wide flowers on the limestone pavement below the mountain. The rare untidy Jacob's Ladder still colours the slope of loose stone under the cliff at Malham Cove, as Ray noted in 1696. Rarity, in fact, has driven botanists, with a black tin case in one hand, into every ditch of Great Britain and Ireland from Teesdale to Killarney ; and rarity has given botanists their best, and most inconclusive, argument. Why are some plants rare ? How is it some plants manage to hang on in a place or two, increasing or decreasing a little, or just keeping up a slender population, year in, year out ? Here and there a few arctic, or alpine, plants hang on ; in the south and south-west and in Ireland grow here and there plants (such as the Cornish moneywort) which belong to the Mediterranean neighbourhood, or the ocean side of France, and Spain, and Portugal, and North Africa.

The first plant of this kind I was ever taken to see was *Lobelia urens*— a plant far too rare ever to get a name for itself in ordinary English. I was fourteen. We cycled solemnly as though to a shrine, to the place where it had been discovered in the nineteenth century by two ladies. The landmarks, a tree, a cottage, a gateway, were established. We climbed the hedge, and there, in a damp scrubby corner of alders and bramble grew plenty of this, as I remember it, rather mincing and elegant plant expressing itself in a few small blue flowers. It was nothing like so strange as the abundant water lobelia, which I never saw till I stood among its flowers years later in the fringes of a lake under Slieve League, in Donegal. The water lobelia grows its leaves under water, and sends its flower stems nakedly up from a few inches depth into the air ; but the rarity, the aura, the reputation of this other lobelia, only known at that time in Dorset and Cornwall, would have turned a much duller plant into one of the images of life. There were other species called 'Lusitanian,' or 'Atlantic,' or 'Oceanic,' to be found in Cornwall, most obviously the acres-wide Cornish heath (*Erica vagans*) on the soil over the barren serpentine rock of the Lizard, a plant which belongs more abundantly to Turkey and Greece and the Mediterranean and Spain.

Some botanists say the arctic plants survived in spots which were not covered in the last period of glaciation. The various southern species, they also argue, survived this last frozen period from a warmer time which preceded it. Have they survived, or are they emigrés, adventurers, who came here after the ice diminished and disappeared ?

To choose, not emotionally altogether, between the two sides, I would come down on immigration with Professor Salisbury. He thinks the whole climate must have been too cold for these tenderer plants during

HERB PARIS
Coloured engraving after a drawing by James Sowerby 1756–1822
From Sowerby's *English Botany*
By courtesy of the Royal Horticultural Society

HIMALAYAN BALSAM: *IMPATIENS GLANDULIFERA*
Coloured engraving after a drawing by Miss Drake
From Lindley's *Botanical Register*, 1840
By courtesy of the Royal Horticultural Society

CHEDDAR PINK
Drawing by E. W. Hunnybun

the period of ice. He thinks, also, that man may have had something to do with their presence. He is worth quoting on that :

"If we bear in mind the successive waves of human invaders upon these islands, we cannot help but be struck by the fact that the colonization from Western and Mediterranean Europe took place in the warm moist epoch at the close of the Atlantic period . . . If we compare the distribution of the megalithic monuments in Western Europe . . . with that of the mass distribution of the oceanic element in our flora . . . , we shall realize that megalithic man colonised the area over which these plants occur to-day, and these people may therefore quite possibly have been important agents in the dispersal of seeds."

It would be a good way to come in as a seed on the clothing of the men who built Avebury and Stanton Drew, or in the grain they brought with them, or in a speck of mud on the foot of one of their animals. And botanists who insist, less romantically on the ice-age survival theory, have against them one thing among several—a great mass of extraordinary evidence about the ways in which seeds are always on the move through the world—through men, by sea, in the air, attached to birds' feet, and even on dragonflies' wings. About all this, there is a *magnum opus* of fascination, H. N. Ridley's *Dispersal of Plants Throughout The World*. Ridley's furthest record of the flight of a winged seed is from the Chilean Andes across the Atlantic to Tristan d'Acunha—5,500 miles. Seeds can float 1,000 miles by sea, and be ready to germinate when they come to land ; but, if they are to develop, they must come from plants able to grow and establish themselves in a salty habitat. Tropical seeds come to Ireland via the Gulf Stream and the North Atlantic Drift in a fit state to do their job, if only the climate were warm enough. Estimating that a pigeon can fly continuously at thirty miles an hour, and assuming that a pigeon fed on small seeded fruits before it started, and did not pass them all for four hours, Ridley showed that a seed could be carried by a pigeon for 120 miles. Seeds will pass unharmed through a pigeon, or for that matter, through a man. In England tomato plants come up on sewage farms, and prickly pear from the New World has been spread round the Mediterranean by men eating the fruit and passing the seeds. But outside rather than inside, we take seeds with us everywhere. Shepherd's purse, dandelion, groundsel, couch-grass, and burdock seeds found their way out from England to New England in the seventeenth century. Groundsel has gone out to Java with European vegetable seeds, and has done very well there for itself. Scottish emigrants are reputed to have taken heather beds with them to Nova Scotia, and so heather seeds, which germinated. There are two stories in Ridley's book which show exactly how various plants might have come into England with Palaeolithic hunters, let alone the Neolithic, and Bronze Age, and Iron Age, and later peoples from Europe, who tilled the ground. The first is his story of the Sakais, wild tribes who lives up country in the Malay Peninsula. They seldom cultivate anything, he says, "but I have found in the Pahang forests, far from any cultivation, *Colocasia antiquorum* (cultivated in the lowlands, and probably of Polynesian origin), *Pogostemon Heyneanus*, of Indian origin, and *Clerodendron paniculatum*, a favourite plant with the Sakai girls, who gather pieces of the scarlet panicles to decorate their hair, and plant them near their temporary camps. All these plants were growing together, having been carried from afar by these wild folk." In Malay, there is a lost world, the Gunong Tahan plateau, with precipices round it which had prevented the Sakais from climbing into it, and had kept out all the larger animals except wild goats. In 1905 or 1906, it was first explored by a European, and he found no bracken growing there at all. In 1910 Ridley got up on to the plateau, and found several plants of bracken growing by the hut which the first expedition had occupied. The spores had obviously come in on the rice sacks or the baggage.

If seeds of plants such as the lobelia I mentioned or the Cornish heath, or the strawberry tree in Ireland, or the yellow bartsia which covers a great many meadows down in Cornwall, arrived with the megalith builders when the climate was at its best for them, a slight shift in temperature might have cut them down and restricted them to a few extra favourable places. Some of the South-western rarities, that lobelia for one, seem to be increasing slightly, perhaps because of the slightly increased mildness of our winter climate since the turn of this century. *Lobelia urens* is now in Hampshire, Devon, and Herefordshire, as well as in Cornwall and Dorset.

Rare plants apart, a rough date, arrived at upon evidence of various kinds, has been decided for the early introduction of a good many plants into England. In *The Origin of the British Flora* (1899), Clement Reid, of the Geological Survey collected some results of examining early deposits for relics of seed and plant. Fumitory had been found in Neolithic deposits, and not before, with several other weeds of cultivated land. Corn marigold was one of them. Two others were cornflower and corn spurrey. Mountain ash and pear and damson also cropped up in Neolithic deposits for the first

DANDELION
Wood-engraving by Bewick
1753-1828

23

time. Penny-cress and the small poppy, *Papaver argemone*, did not occur except in Roman levels. The Romans have been held responsible for handing down several other plants, the box for one. And also the greater celandine. It is true that five greater celandine seeds were found in an interglacial deposit in Sussex. But celandine only grows in England now in relationship with man and his activities and dwellings. It has not, any more than corn marigold, or fumitory, or corn flower, an independent habitat over here, and without man it would probably disappear. White dead nettle, which is held to be native in woods and forests from Spain and Morocco to Siberia and the Himalayas, is another weed which has gone about with men. It likes the constantly renewed soil thrown up from a ditch, and it probably settled in England as a colonist. A good thing too, because its beaked regular flowers and neat, strong habit make it a weed to look at and like, and pick, and put in one's house. It is worth turning a dead nettle upside down to admire the remarkable pattern made by the four yellow and black anthers against the pure white of the flower's hood.

SETTLERS' IN BRITAIN

ACCURATE plant records do not go very far back ; and all that I have said leads up to those particular species—some of them exceedingly fine—whose record as settlers in Great Britain we really do know.

One of them is the ivy-leaved toadflax, the Mother-of-Thousands which hangs from the crannies now of nine old walls in ten, in cities as well as out, all through the country. Its home was Southern Europe and Switzerland and the Tyrol—Ruskin points to it in rock clefts in pictures by Bellini—and Englishmen in the seventeenth century, or else before that, introduced it into English gardens. It was not content. In Hertfordshire it was growing outside gardens as early as 1640. By the end of the eighteenth century it had spread all around London. William Curtis wrote in the *Flora Londinensis* (1798) "it is found in great plenty in all those parts near London, that lay within the reach of the Thames ; the seeds are carried by the flux and reflux of the tide up and down the river, and left at high water mark in the crevices of old walls, where they take root and increase very fast." It was still not a common plant in Cornwall in 1804, and the Cornish President of the Royal Society, Davies Gilbert, did the very human and likeable thing so much disliked by botanists of the older kind (who think plants were only made for them and science) : he planted ivy-leaved toadflax on St. Michael's Mount. If you are a garden plant you are regarded, well regarded, just as long as you stay in the garden. Go outside, go on to the streets, and you lose your repu-

YELLOW FLAG

Coloured engraving from Redouté's *Les Liliacées*, 1808

By courtesy of the Sherardian Professor of Botany, University of Oxford

GREATER CELANDINE

Coloured engraving after a drawing by William Delamotte 1775–1863

From Baxter's *British Flowering Plants,* 1839

By courtesy of the President and Fellows of Magdalen College, Oxford

tation. Still, the ivy-leaved toadflax has earned a good many names by its rapid multiplication, of which I like best the name "Roving Sailor." It found a place to live where there was no, or not very much, competition; and suitable walls no doubt greatly increased with the enclosure of land and the extensive new building of the eighteenth and nineteenth centuries.

Not every plant has been as lucky. Think of the vast number of seeds which are on the move. Seeds of different plants come in from most countries of the world, at every port, in every kind of way, mixed up with corn, clinging to hides, twisted up in wool.

Here in England, there is a common Canadian plant, Canadian Flea-bane, first noted in 1690, and now doing very well on bombed sites in London. The first seed of the first plant of Canadian fleabane is said— and it may be true—to have dropped out of the stuffing of a bird. If you recall the figures I quoted, there were, in 1931, held to be 1,799 plants growing in Great Britain which came from abroad, but had not established themselves. Some are cornfield weeds, which come in with grain, much as the first seeds of corn marigold came in in Neolithic times. Some arrive with seed for canaries and budgerigars. A classic place for a changing population of alien, or at least imperial, plants, is the tweed making district of Tweedside. An Australian going to Galashiels in summer would see a good many familiar plants, particularly a tall ragwort, *Senecio lautus*, which seeds itself and can live through the winter ; and a small trailing plant, *Acaena anserinifolia*, with leaves like silverweed, and crimson flowers, which grows on the banks of the Tweed. They both grow from seeds which come over in Australian wool. Many of these wool plants live only for a short time. Their seeds do not ripen soon enough or else the winter is too hard, or the competition of other plants too severe. It is not easy for a species to find room to live, even if it can stand the climate. In a garden, it is one thing: there is little competition, but a foreign plant which tries to get out of a garden, or one that comes in at a sea-port, has to face the close trade union of plants well adapted to temperature, and damp-ness and soil. In the port, on a heap of ballast or a bit of newly turned waste, the plant may find a home where, for the time being, it can spread and thrive. But not far or long ; and it is surprising—till you calculate the difficulties—how few of all the thousands of species that have come and grown for a bit, or have been grown for gardens—how few of them all have ever established an independent and easy life of their own. The sycamore has managed it between now and the sixteenth century when it was introduced, (the sycamore "is nowhere found wilde or naturall in our Land that I can learn, but onely planted in orchards or walkes for the shadowes sake," Parkinson, *Theatrum Botanicum* 1640), and some other species now seem to be making a job of it. Think how well the difficulties are displayed by the odd tale of the Inelegant, or Oxford, ragwort. In-elegant is not quite true : *Senecio squalidus* looks like groundsel on a bigger scale, with better branchings and a handsomer flower. It is an uncommon plant abroad, and likes the volcanic cinders of Etna and Vesuvius. In 1699 a specimen was growing in the Botanic Garden, at Oxford. Seeds grew on a wall or two (you can still see the plant on Oxford walls, for instance in Queen's Lane), but it wasn't really happy. It was first seen on the walls in 1794. By 1877 it got down to the railway, having moved less than two miles in nearly two hundred years. But it found the railway sidings were laid on clinker. In other words, it had got back from the Botanic Garden to the sides of Etna, and it went ramping up and down the railways, settling on the clinker which was empty and unsettled. Its seeds, each with a plume of soft hairs, move with the rush of wind from the trains, and Claridge Druce watched some of them taking an actual railway journey. They floated into a carriage at Oxford and floated out again at Tilehurst. It got to Swindon by 1890 and as far north as Denbighshire by 1916. It has managed to get over to Eire, and has gone along the railway from Cork to Dublin. Since the war it has spread to a slightly different cindery home—into 56% of the burned and bombed sites in London, as the fourth commonest plant, according to Professor Salisbury's account, after rosebay willow-herb and groundsel.

A submerged water-weed, *Naias graminea*, that belongs to warm, still water in the tropics, found its extraordinary way into a Lancashire canal—the right canal, which is warmed up by the hot water coming out of a mill. Of the settlers which have spread, several are not very conspicuous plants or not very lovely ones. The Oxford ragwort displays itself boldly enough, and gives colour to places which need it, but there is no more to claim for it. "Red Betty," the red valerian of walls (*Kentranthus ruber*), always irritates me as being blousy, loud, obtrusive and coarse. The colour is not pleasurable and when many plants grow together they blossom out of an untidy mess of leafage. It is a plant which belongs to the south of Europe, the Lebanon, and elsewhere, but it has been growing outside gardens, at any rate in England, since 1778, when it was recorded on old walls and ruins in Devon and Cornwall. Since then it has reached New Zealand at one end and Iceland at the other, and it is no very good acquisition for us or for them. To look at all well, it needs a large-scale habitat. Walls are not big enough ; but it does almost succeed on the great cliffs of the grey Cheddar Gorge. Another coarse, tough, pushing, persistent settler, is the tall Japanese knotweed (*Polygonum cuspidatum*), which has emerged from the gardens into which it ought never to have been introduced. There is a scrap of morbid attraction about its zigzagging blotchy stems, and the way it forms a gang of plants holding to a slimy patch of shade, an area basement, a corner of Hampstead Heath, or the railway side in Bradford.

But, of all the settlers, there are two which have established themselves much more commonly—two which are so excellent that they need to have

Antirrhinum Cymbalaria.

IVY-LEAVED TOADFLAX
Coloured engraving from Curtis's *Flora Londinensis*, 1777-1798

their stories told. I have mentioned one of them, the monkey-flower (*Mimulus guttatus*). The other is the gigantic balsam (*Impatiens glandulifera*), which has come to England and Ireland from Kashmir and the Western Himalayas. Both have entered by way of gardens. And both are plants which seem to prefer the clarity of a running stream.

The first person to describe monkey-flower as it deserves, was W. H. Hudson in *Hampshire Days*. According to him, country-people in Hampshire called it wild musk. Hudson said "there is no purer, no more beautiful yellow in any of our wild flowers, from the primrose and the almost equally pale, exquisite blossom which we improperly name 'dark

27

mullein' . . . to the intensest pure yellow of the marsh marigold." The charm, he said, was in the colour "and the way in which Nature has disposed it, abundantly in single, separate blossoms, amongst leaves of a green that is rich and beautiful, and looks almost dark by contrast with that shining luminous hue it sets off so well."

In 1812, says Loudon, it was first grown here as a garden plant, having come from streams on the Pacific side of North America. By 1824, it was growing wild in the burn at Invergowrie, near Dundee, in Scotland, and by a mountain stream near Abergavenny in Wales. By 1830 it was flourishing on the banks of the Avon near Salisbury. In a hundred years more, it had conquered ; and its clarity and moistness were frequent over most of the British Isles, from Cornwall to the Shetlands. In Professor Salisbury's *East Anglian Flora* (1932), there is a map of its spread and its great distribution, (a little inaccurate, because East Cornwall had it 25 years ago) ; and H. N. Ridley has investigated the actual way in which it increases. He discovered that monkey-flower seeds float for a few days, absorb water and then sink. By that time they would no doubt have moved a good way. Then the seeds germinate at the bottom of the water, and the seedlings come up and float still further with the current, until they fetch up on a good spot to root and grow. That is how monkey-flower has prevailed in just over a century. Hudson seems only to have known it with flowers entirely yellow, but sometimes they have red blotches, which is how I first knew them in Cornwall, round a pit in which a waterwheel was decaying, or how I have seen it lately in Lonsdale, or on meadows at the foot of Whernside, in West Riding. In one of these meadows, it made a band of colour down a watercourse, visible three miles away.

It seems to like best clean, clear water, and will often make a little island of yellow in quite swift shallows. I came across it like that last summer in a quick stream hurrying down a valley in Wiltshire, in a coralline district where it is rather scarce. I took some home, and learned something else about monkey-flower, that though its flowers are tender, it picks up wonderfully well in a bowl of water, and will last for weeks, opening single blossom after blossom, and spreading a good feeling through the house. In Ireland, I have seen it covering the floor of a withy bed in a dark, mountainy part of Donegal.

Professor Salisbury contrasts monkey-flower with other settlers which can only survive in conditions—for example, in cornfields, or on the railway clinker of the Oxford ragwort—which are kept going artificially. Monkey-flower, he says, occurs as part of a natural community of plants. So, I should think, does the giant balsam of the Himalayas. The balsam was described, in 1839, in Royle's *Illustrations of the Botany of the Himalayan Mountains*, a fine book with illustrations by an Indian artist. By 1840 it had come over to England as a garden plant, and was first recorded as establishing itself outside gardens by 1855. Of our four balsams, two others are also successful immigrants, *Impatiens fulva*, tall and orange, from North America, and the smaller, rather scant *Impatiens parviflora*, which comes from Russia, and is common as a weed, for example, in London and round the edges of Hampstead Heath. Two American names for *Impatiens fulva* are "kicking colt" from the typical way in which its seeds kick out, and "speckled jewels." I first knew the Himalayan balsam in the East Looe valley in Cornwall. When A. O. Hume saw it there in 1900, he wrote a picture in the *Journal of Botany* which is very true :

> "I notice that it has been called 'a cumbersome and weedy thing'; but growing in the soft, warm south-west, with the base of its stem in the clear running stream, it is a magnificent plant, 5-7 feet, or more, in height, stalwart, with a stem from one to one and a half inches in diameter just above the surface of the water, erect, symmetrical in shape, with numerous aggregations of blossom, the central mass as big as a man's head, and those terminating all the principal lateral branches, though smaller, still most striking—masses of bloom varying in different plants through a dozen lovely shades of colour from the very palest pink imaginable to the deepest claret colour, and with a profusion of large, elegant, dark green, lance-olate leaves, some of them fully 15 inches in length."

From June to autumn, its pink bank and billows of flower fill the valley beside the railway and the stream with a wide gentleness of colour ; and the plant is spreading far beyond Cornwall and the Devonshire rivers. It is moving in Somerset, in Derbyshire, in Ireland, on the Liffey, in Sligo, and elsewhere; starting right in the city, miles of it are visible in the canal which runs beside the railway line

Ophrys apifera

BEE ORCHIS
Engraving by W. Kilburn
1745-1818

29

from Leeds towards Skipton ; but, for all the notice given to it in popular flower books, it might still be hiding away 7,000 ft. up in the western Himalayas instead of flaunting so deliciously and prominently in English and Irish valleys.

For a hundred years, writers have commented on the botanical assumption that plants which have recently escaped or been introduced, are disreputable, invisible, and no part of the landscape. They do not, in fact, exist. "I do not see why we should make laws to exclude plants because we fancy we have witnessed their introduction," wrote someone more sensible than his fellows in *The Phytologist*, commenting in 1848 on the spread of monkey-flower ; and when Hudson wrote *Hampshire Days* in 1923, and wanted to find out about monkey-flower, he went to the books and found that some did not mention it, and some dismissed it "with the remark that it is an 'introduced plant'." It is hard to think that the attitude which causes all this, is anything but selfish, and pseudo-scientific.

Rhododendron ponticum, the ordinary rhododendron, seeds itself abundantly in many places, a very different state of things to its appearance in a magnificent plate, in 1812, among the rare exotics of Dr. Thornton's "Temple of Flora." *Mesembryanthemum equilaterale*, the mesembryanthemum which Cornish people pleasantly corrupt into "Sally-my-handsome," densely cloaks acres of English cliff, and spreads across the anchovy-sauce rocks of Dawlish and Teignmouth. But flower books do not acknowledge one or the other.

COUNTY FLORAS AND COMMON FLOWERS

NONE can interest himself very far in plants, without having to consult the flora of the county he lives in. They are delightful books, these county floras, out-of-date most of them, necessarily incomplete, and the romantic product of the exploring, collecting habit, and an older, more elementary aim in botanical studies. To the specialist they now indicate, very roughly, only how plants are, or were, distributed. But they feed the ordinary man's emotion. They tell him where to look for the rarities, and if they crop up elsewhere, he gets the extra pleasure of finding rare plants in places where the floras have not recorded them. They give him—or most of them do—a history of plant-hunting in each county, going back to the records of the early botanists, Turner, Gerard, Johnston, Parkinson, Ray, and often including pious sketches of the life and botanical work in each county of long dead eccentric parsons or doctors, who botanised on their visiting and rounds.

Much of what the floras have to say about climate and geology is inaccurate or beside the point, and they have some irritating restrictions and

Arum maculatum

LORDS-AND-LADIES
Coloured engraving from Curtis's *Flora Londinensis*, 1777-1798

conventions which persist even in some of the more recent of them—that superiority, for example, to any plant which has only the record of recent introduction or naturalisation, and not the pedigree of a native. But all these sins may be forgiven, for there are no better books to take on a holiday into a new part of England. It is not only the rare plants that they guide you towards : read through a flora and it gives you an idea at once of what plants you may find which are common in one locality, but perhaps altogether rare around your home. If you live in Yorkshire, for instance, and you are going to have a holiday in Cornwall, Davey's *Flora of Cornwall* will show you that you will find pennywort growing on every wall, tutsan, the large and lovely shrubby St. John's Wort, common on the earth hedges, and a good many other plants as abundant there as they are scarce in Yorkshire. If you live in Cornwall and are going up to the West Riding, looking through Lees's *Flora of West Yorkshire* will inform you that lady's mantle will be one of the commonest wayside plants up there, that in many places you will walk by river banks covered with the mauve-pink of bird's-eye primrose, that you will find the livid purple and orange flower of water avens hanging in all the damp angles under the limestone walls, that many of the mountain meadows and dale meadows will be pink with bistort, that you will see tall stems of great throatwort (*Campanula latifolia*), which exudes a white juice when you break it, standing up beside the mountain woods. A Sussex flora would introduce to a Yorkshireman, for the first time, locally common plants like hounds-tongue, the leaves of which smell like mice, or gladdon, the stinking iris, which is lovelier in orange seed in early winter than it is in flower, or the dwarf thistle with its head hunched in the ground, which is rare in the limestone valleys of West Yorkshire as the tall melancholy thistle (*Carduus heterophyllus*) is common.

All this is why county floras are so necessary to supplement the ordinary flower books, which are either topographically rather partisan, or else try to strike an average and so leave out plants which may be common in one area but scarce in others. As a Cornishman and a Southerner, for example, I find Professor Skene's *Flower Book For The Pocket* partisan. Professor Skene is a Scotsman. He illustrates many flowers you will find in Scotland and the North—globe-flower, moss-campion, the very charming little bog stonecrop, wintergreen, linnaea—which is excellent; but he leaves out a good many plants you are likely to see in the south and the west—*Ornithogalum umbellatum*, for example, the graceful individual Star-of-Bethlehem, which is common enough in North Somerset to be sold every year by Bath greengrocers as wild asparagus. Tutsan, and yellow bartsia, he mentions, but does not think worth illustrating. Cornish moneywort is not mentioned, nor is bastard balm (*Melittis Melissophyllum*), which is a plant thousands of visitors must see every year in Devon and Cornwall. Last May I walked down a lane in Cornwall in which the

PRIMROSES
Detail from "Primroses and Bird's Nest"
Oil painting by William Hunt, 1790–1864
By courtesy of the Tate Gallery

ROSEBAY WILLOWHERB

Coloured engraving after a drawing by James Sowerby 1756–1822

From Sowerby's *English Botany*

By courtesy of the Royal Horticultural Society

hedges were white and
purple-pink with balm
on either side for two
miles.

One more thing about
common plants–the very
common plants. There
is a temptation to grow
blasé about them, to
yearn only for rarities,
in the manner of the
stamp collector. I do
find it unnecessary to
look much at some of the
dingy ubiquitous plants,
which are to other plants
as sparrows are to red-
starts and kingfishers, or
even to chiffchaffs and
thrushes. But I try to
keep my eyes clear. The
thing is to look every
season at harebells, for
example, or the blue
wheels of chicory, or the
sprawling fine pattern of
fumitory, or the cut delicacy of musk mallow, or
the superb scarlet berries
of lords-and-ladies, as
though you had never
seen them before.

WRITING ABOUT
FLOWERS

RAGGED ROBIN
Engraving after John Henderson, 1810

APART from all the
floras of every kind
and scope, English
flowers—and it is a good thing—have never been too much, or too well
written about, at length. There is not much flower writing com-
parable to the writing about birds. There have not been any botanical
Gilbert Whites or Lord Greys, and flowers have been left pretty well

33

alone, to be well-liked objects of nature, objects of a private treasure hunt, and to be part of the imagery of the human mind. Not so much can be thought into flowers. So their virtue has not been cheapened, they have not been run down into a cult, which begins at last to affect human beings badly. Birds, like dogs, can retard an Englishman and keep him as undeveloped as a child, just past the stage of egg-collecting. Flowers have never been allowed to become quite so sentimentally, dangerously powerful. But their influence does remain constant, does remain strong, and unobtrusively good. And if one made an anthology of English writing about flowers, one would find them occasionally described, and symbolically used, one would find flower bits here and there, but discover few long flower chapters or flower poems, except during a mid-nineteenth century period of ladyism.

Ruskin, who wrote skilfully about flowers himself, carefully thought about the way they affect us. He said that flowers had no sublimity:

"... impressions of awe and sorrow being at the root of the sensation of sublimity and the beauty of separate flowers not being of the kind which connects itself with such sensation, there is a wide distinction in general, between

13 *Ranunculus globosus.*
Locker Goulons, or globe Crowfoote.

❊ *The description.*

13 The globe Crowfoote hath verie manie leaues deepely cut and iagged, of a bright green colour, like those of the field Crowfoot: among which riseth vp a stalke, diuided towarde the top into other branches, furnished with the like leaues of those next the grounde, but smaller: on the tops of which branches growe very faire yellowe flowers, consisting of a fewe leaues, folded or rowled vp togither like a round ball or globe; whereupon it was called *Ranunculus globosus,* or the globe Crowfoote, or globe flower, which being past, there succeede rough knaps, wherein is blackish seed: the roote is small and threddy.

❊ *The place.*
This kinde of Crowfoote groweth in most places of Yorkeshire, and Lancashire, and other those bordering shires of the North countrey, almost in euery medowe, but not found wilde in these southerly or westerly parts of Englande, that I could euer vnderstand of.
❊ *The time.*
It flowreth in Maie and Iune. The seed is ripe in August.

GLOBE FLOWER
Detail from a page of Gerard's Herball, 1597

flower-loving minds, and minds of the largest order. Flowers seem intended for the solace of ordinary humanity : children love them ; quiet, tender, contented people love them as they grow, luxurious and disorderly people rejoice in them gathered : they are the cottager's treasure and in the crowded town, mark, as with a little broken fragment of rainbow, the windows of the workers in whose hearts rests the contentment of peace. Passionate or religious minds contemplate them with fond, feverish intensity ; the affection is seen severely calm in the works of many old religious painters, and mixed with more open and true country sentiment in those of our own Pre-Raphaelites. To the child, and the girl, and the peasant and the manufacturing operative, to the grisette and the nun, the lover and monk, they are precious always. But to the men of supreme power and thoughtfulness, precious only at times ; symbolically and pathetically often to the poets, but rarely for their sake. They fall forgotten from the great workmen's and soldiers' hands. Such men will take, in thankfulness, crowns of leaves, or crowns of thorns—not crowns of flowers . . ."

COMMON MALLOW
Engraving after J. Sowerby, 1756-1822

It is a good passage and worth remembering so long as it does not set the reader fancying he must always act like the man of supreme power, and thinking he must always reject flowers for an everlasting tornado of eternal truths, always eat tragedy and reject all the minute lyrical entertainments.

Our ordinary relation to flowers comes out in the affectionate, observant and often very attractive and satisfying names we have given them. W. H. Hudson was delighted by a name he heard for the yellow stonecrop "Welcome-home-husband-though-never-so-drunk," which obviously derives from the vividness of its yellow welcome on a yard wall or on a sloping back-kitchen roof. Professor Salisbury has recorded a good name for moschatel—"Town Hall Clock," because four of its five flowers look out, like clock faces, from the sides of a cube, and he complains that very often the garden plant has not been so aptly named as the wild flower. I should say the reason is that most of the garden plants have come in during the last hundred years and have been named in a period, or by a class, without passion. Many popular names go back to the sixteenth century, to a period of supreme verbal happiness and strength, and many of the names actually invented by the early botanists have a glint and a propriety which a garden plant could not hope to acquire from a literary, dilute, devitalised, middle-class English.

Here are names invented or recorded by William Turner, mostly between 1538 and 1548 : King-cup, leopard's bane, spindle-tree, loose-strife, daffodil (earlier it was "affodil," that is to say, asphodel), lady's tresses, bindweed, crane's-bill, goat's-beard, wintergreen, butcher's broom, hornbeam. Names cropping up between 1525 and 1538 are wood-sorrel (not an improvement on the earlier 'woodsour'), meadowsweet, bugloss, eyebright, pellitory, forget-me-not. The biggest list of innovations comes from Henry Lyte's *Niewe herball or historie of plantes*, which was a trans-lation from the Dutch (1578). Lyte's names include bistort, speedwell, Herb Paris, campion, buckbean, toadflax, willow-herb, silver-weed, Devil's milk (wood-spurge), sundew, live-long, monkshood and twayblade. Gerard's recorded names (1597) include burdock and wayfaring tree, and among garden plants, honesty and Turks Cap (which in those days meant a tulip). Snapdragon is Elizabethan, and I would choose "Grim the

WILLOW AND WILD ROSES
Detail from 'Ophelia,' by Sir John Millais, 1829-1896

36

OLD MAN'S BEARD AND THISTLE IN SEED
Detail from 'The Stonebreaker,' by John Brett, 1831-1902

Collier" as one particular sample from the sixteenth or seventeenth century. It is the name for *Hieraceum aurianticum*, which has now dug itself firmly into various countries, and various places in this country, outside the gardens for which it was introduced. "The stalkes and cups of the flowres are all set thicke with a blackish downe or hairinesse as it were the duste of coles ; whence the women who keep it in gardens for noveltie sake, have named it Grim the Colliar" (Johnson's revision—1633—of Gerard's *Herball*). At times we are told that no natural thing was ever *seen* and freshly and accurately described much before 1800. These herbal names prove that to be wrong. Many are good description, nearly all are good-shaped words marked by what Christopher Smart called "the beauty, force and vehemence of *Impression* . . . a talent or a gift of Almighty God by which a Genius is empowered to throw an emphasis upon a word or sentence in such wise, that it cannot escape any reader of sheer good sense, and true critical sagacity."

By contrast with these sixteenth century names (and the older, mediaeval names as well), you can see our poverty from a seed catalogue, or from running through the names on any few pages of Bentham and Hooker —hispid althaea, tuberous pea, reflexed-leaved stonecrop, and so on. It

37

is sweetening after that dose to think of names like old man's beard for *Clematis Vitalba*, Solomon's seal (1543) for *Polygonatum multiflorum*, moonlight for the chervil (*Chaerophyllum sylvestre*) filling lanes for 200 yards at a length with blossom, pale and extensive like its name, lady's white petticoats for the delicacy and silk and satin whiteness of stitchwort, devil's cherries for the black, shining fruits of the deadly nightshade, yellow spit for the greater celandine, from its yellow juice, and look-up-and-kiss-me for the heartsease.

Leaving imaginative names and coming to flowers used with imagination by writers, here, to explain one use, is a Pre-Raphaelite poem from Coventry Patmore's *Angel in the House* :

> Not in the crisis of events,
>   Of compass'd hopes, or fear fulfill'd
> Or acts of gravest consequence,
>   Are life's delight and depth reveal'd.
> The day of days was not the day ;
>   That went before, or was postponed ;
> The night Death took our lamp away
>   Was not the night on which we groan'd.
> I drew my bride, beneath the moon,
>   Across my threshold, happy hour !
> But, ah, the walk that afternoon
>   We saw the water-flags in flower !

A symbol, a statement, no description ; only a reminder, with emotion heaped on, of a common sight.

But perhaps it would be best to turn this comment on the employment and enjoyment of flowers into a flower anthology. So I shall begin, after a piece of Ruskin, with four writers who knew much about plants, Crabbe, Clare, Lord de Tabley (who had a passion for brambles, with their almost abstract differences, and compiled a *Flora of Cheshire*), and Andrew Young, who has seen most of the rare plants of England.

ANTHOLOGY, OR FLOWER PICKING

Gather a green poppy bud, just when it shows the scarlet line at its side ; break it open and unpack the poppy. The whole flower is there complete in size and colour—its stamens full grown, but all packed so closely that the fine silk of the petals is crushed into a million of shapeless wrinkles. When the flower opens, it seems a deliverance from torture : the two imprisoning green leaves are shaken to the ground ; the aggrieved corolla smoothes itself in the sun, and comforts itself as it can ; but remains visibly crushed and hurt to the end of its days.

John Ruskin

Even such direct, deliberate description bears the double meaning of an image. Crabbe's flowers are the careful foreground of a large-scale

FOXGLOVE
Engraving after a drawing by Sydenham Edwards, 1769-1819
From Thornton's *Elementary Botanical Plates*, 1810

landscape with a sentiment of foreboding and gloom, bugloss on sterile ground, henbane faded and nauseous smelling in the sun, yet both lovely and held in the mind, as firmly as the mussels and the mud banks and the tide sliding away in Crabbe's story of Peter Grimes. And Crabbe's flowers are

ECOLOGY, OR FLOWERS IN A GROUP

. . There, fed by food they love, to rankest size
Around the dwellings docks and wormwood rise ;
Here the strong mallow strikes her slimy root,
Here the dull nightshade hangs her deadly fruit ;
On hills of dust the henbane's faded green,
And pencil'd flower of sickly scent is seen ;
At the walls' base the fiery nettle springs,
With fruit globose and fierce with poison'd stings ;
Above (the growth of many a year) is spread
The yellow level of the stonecrop's bed ;
In every chink delights the fern to grow,
With glossy leaf and tawny bloom below :
These with our sea-weeds, rolling up and down,
Form the contracted flora of the town . . .

Then Clare. There is a vast, limp amount of herbage in the two big volumes of Clare's poetry, which came out a few years ago. Except that the herbage shines clearer and is more exactly held, it sometimes gets as dull as those plants Richard Jefferies often translated with no particular purpose out of a Wiltshire field into a chapter. Then Clare began to turn his transcriptions into a simultaneous reality and symbol—for example, love living within itself like a wild flower in its own scent. And before they finish, poets such as Clare and Holderlin can make a whole wood and a whole time of year and a whole statement of life in the way they use an adjective like green or blue. In Clare's eyes flowers began to burn, especially during his first madness in Epping Forest :

Daisies burn April grass with silver fires,
And pilewort in the green lane blazes out
Enough to burn the fingers, 'neath the briers . . .

According to his son, Crabbe "cultivated botany, especially that of the grasses, with insatiable ardour." Lord de Tabley's botany was also pretty exact, as you can see in his *Flora of Cheshire*, in which are included several of his poems :

From AN OCEAN GRAVE

. . But patches of the seapink shine
The tired crows poise and come ;
The mallow hangs, the bindweeds twine,
Where her sweet lips are dumb . . .

DOG ROSE
Coloured engraving by A. Parsons 1847–1920
From E. Willmott's *The Genus Rosa*.

MONKEY-FLOWER

Coloured engraving after a drawing by Sydenham Edwards, c. 1769–1819

From Curtis's *Botanical Magazine,* 1812

By courtesy of the Royal Horticultural Society

Come hither, linnets tufted-red,
  Drift by, O wailing tern ;
Set pure vale-lilies at her head,
  At her feet lady-fern.

Grow, samphire, at the tidal brink,
  Wave, pansies of the shore,
To whisper how alone I think
  Of her for evermore.

Bring blue sea-hollies, thorny, keen,
  Long lavender in flower
Grey wormwood like a hoary queen,
  Stanch mullein like a tower. . .

De Tabley's flowers are later nineteenth century, a calling up of colour.
Their job is to make up part of rather a hazy, coloured mood and scene,
like flowers in a wild herbaceous border.

NIGHT-FLOWERING CAMPION

Close on the bat-crossed hour
I waited for a flower
By light grown visible
Burning the vivid hill.

Pimpernel in night bud
Showed like small drops of blood ;
It was no common flower
I kept late vigil for.

I watched by falling light
Till I saw how with white
And patient petals shone
Night-flowering campion.

So white those petals showed
And such a rich scent flowed,
I said, "Are we not one,
I and this campion ?"

Seeing how for us both
Sweetness followed on sloth
I felt my own song's power
In that urgent flowering flower.

But when I came that way
In the clear light of day
I noticed a mean plant
Sticky and small and scant.

                                    A. J. Young

41

Next, ash flowers from the notebooks of Gera d Hopkins :

The male ashes are very boldly jotted with the heads of the bloom which tuft the outer ends of the branches. . . When the bud breaks at first it shews a heap of fruity purplish anthers looking something like unripe elder-berries but these push open into richly branched tree-pieces coloured buff and brown, shaking out loads of pollen, and drawing the tuft as a whole into peaked quains —mainly four, I think, two bigger and two smaller.

The bushes in the woods and hedgerows are spanned over and twisted upon by the woody cords of the honeysuckle : the cloves of leaf these bear are some purple, some grave green. But the young green of the briars is gay and neat and smooth as if cut in ivory.—One bay or hollow of Hodder Wood is curled all over with bright green garlic.

These Hopkins ash trees lead to three lines of a twelfth century Welsh poem translated by William Barnes :

Bright is the top of the ash, long, and white,
When it grows by the dell.
Long is the sickness of the sad heart.

Leaving aside Shakespeare, the keenest flower poets, I believe, are William Browne, Thomson, Wordsworth,

. . the wild pink crowns the garden-wall,
And with the flowers are intermingled stones
Sparry and bright, rough scatterings of the hills . . .

Cowper, Mickle, Chatterton, Crabbe, Clare, Barnes (read his poems on the yellow water-lily and the water crowfoot), Hopkins, Tennyson, and A. J. Young ; the best prose writers on flowers, James Hervey, Dorothy Wordsworth, Ruskin, and Hudson.

Here is Hudson—a piece for the ivy-stripping archaeologists who rape every ruin they get their official finger-nails on to :

IVY

Is it not well that this plant, this evergreen tapestry of innumerable leaves, should cover and partly hide and partly reveal the "strange defeatures," the centuries have set on man's greatest works ? I would have no ruin, nor no old and noble building without it ; for not only does it beautify decay, but from long association it has come to be in the mind a very part of such scenes, and so interwoven with the human tragedy, that, like the churchyard yew, it seems the most human of green things.

FLOWER CHANGES AND FLOWER BOOKS

GREAT changes are certainly taking place in the community of British flowers, though one need not be either surprised, or, I think, alarmed. We get an idea that such natural changes are a peculiar evil of degenerating modernity, so change causes us much regret when we

MARSH ORCHIS

Engraving after J. Henderson, from Thornton's *Elementary Botanical Plates*, 1810

ought to be grateful for it as the one vitalising, if not always pleasant, condition of life that we cannot avoid. Certain species of plant are diminishing—apparently, Professor Salisbury calculates, about 294 species, or 13% of the total British flora. We are suffering most in plants that like wet or damp places to grow in. There is less water about on the surface of Britain. Marshes have been drained, the vast amount of water taken for cities has lowered the permanent watertable. Roads and drains and ditches are better kept, so water hangs about less and runs off quicker into streams and rivers and into the sea. All this means fewer homes, for example, for bogbean, for royal fern, for the sundews, fritillary, butterwort, bog pimpernel, and so on. Bogbean is a sturdy old inhabitant, which was here, like dandelion, and elder, and bulrush, before the ice ages, and it will be sad if a plant so old and so lovely ever becomes decidedly rare, or—which is less likely—extinct. Since the war, much ditching and draining has been done, and that must hasten the decrease of water-loving species.

When Professor Salisbury made his calculations in 1937, he reckoned that next after water plants 41 species belonging to woodland, or wood margins, or to hedgerows that reproduce woodland conditions, were going downward. Among them are Solomon's seal, the little ivy-leaved bell-flower, and the purple-pink and white bastard balm which, as I have mentioned before, is still common enough in many hedgerows in Devon and Cornwall. Many plants have survived in woodlands kept closed for shooting. The woodland rate of decrease must obviously go up, now when so much hard wood timber is being felled, and so many wood margins have been cleared for victory farming. Hedges also are being grubbed up. Several plants of disturbed soil and cornfield—the plants which live in dependency upon agriculture—have become scarcer. Partly the reason was a smaller acreage of crops, and because various kinds of seeds were better cleaned. But now corn growing has so stupendously increased, I suppose some plants, the seeds of which are not easily separated by screening, may well get more abundant because of the war. Several of the striking seaside and woodland and chalkdown plants, yellow-wort, for example, or wild seakale, do owe their smaller quantity, in some degree, to the way in which people could get around by bicycle and car and motor bicycle and motor coach. Some such species recovered a bit in the last war, and, with traffic off the roads, are pretty certain to do so in this.

And what will be the effects of the cultivation in many places of such fairly scarce medical plants as henbane and deadly nightshade, which we used to import from the Balkans and elsewhere ? One way and the other, whatever human beings do, there is also climate to intervene. If our warmish spell of the last forty years turns into a still warmer average, some of the southern type plants may spread. If it turns colder, some plants which have spread may retract, and some plants hanging on at the limit of their range may vanish except in the most favourable nooks.

We lose and we gain—as we have gained monkey-flower, and the Himalayan balsam. Motorcar parties may damage a bluebell wood, but motor car air-currents along roads undoubtedly help other plants to spread ; and motor cars and cigarettes are given as two indirect causes for the spread

STINKING HELLEBORE
Woodcut by John Nash from his *Poisonous Plants*, 1927

of a plant which is just as striking and as lovely as the bluebell. This is the rosebay willow-herb. It used to be scarce. But it happens to be one of the few plants which will grow with pleasure in recently burnt ground, where the seeds have the light they need for germinating freely, and where wood ash and sterilisation help to produce the nitrates which the willow-herb likes. Cigarette ends and car picnics have meant more heath fires, and so, argues Professor Salisbury, more willow-herb. And if picnics and heath fires are fewer for the time being, burnt out and bombed areas are more abundant for the rosebay to ramp over with the 80,000 parachute seeds a young plant can produce in one season. (Americans, by the way

45

—and this plant of the incendiary bomb and H.E. grows with them from Greenland to Alaska, and Alaska to California—call it "fire-top," and "fire-weed" and "blooming-sally," but we still have no popular name).

The time for us all to worry will be when some malign influence brings it about, that if species die, nothing will succeed them except bald patches of earth. That will be the time to moan about change and decay and degeneration.

Two other things need saying—Gods and men from Persephone downwards always have picked flowers, and it strikes me as mean and foolish and damaging to the sensibilities of the human race to train children to leave all flowers unpicked as they find them. Moderation—no doubt ; but the right of children—and your right and mine—to pick flowers is worth more to humanity than the preservation of a rare plant. Next, if excellent plants threaten to become rare, they should, where it is possible, be reseeded and kept going. This notion has always made some less imaginative experts foolish with rage. For years botanical journals have been spotted with complaint about 'unnatural' interference with the distribution of species. There was rage in the *Journal of Botany* some years ago, after Miss Wilhelmina Stitch had written a Fragrant Minute in the *Daily Sketch*, about seeds : "Hikers ! Please take note ... Must confess that I am smitten with an idea gay and new. Hikers! make a brighter Britain, taking flower seeds out with you. Varied seeds where'er you're going, sow a pinch first here, then there—Nature will attend their growing — Britain

TUFTED VETCH
Water colour by an unknown artist

will look passing fair." Miss Stitch is not an ecologist, and Nature is hardly likely to attend so much as she thinks, but I do not know that Miss Stitch's ignorance was much funnier than the heavy scorn of the learned botanist of the South Kensington Museum. But a botanist wins my first prize, by commenting in 1926, when a school paper had suggested that children should plant hedgerows with seedling ferns or plants they had raised themselves in school, that this dreadful thing would be "to tamper with nature in a thoroughly reprehensible way."

In other words (an odd scientific statement) children and human actions are outside nature ; and nature must be left alone to provide botanists with a private dominion. If such people had their way, no strange flower could ever be put in a garden for fear it escaped, and no human being could wear trousers for fear a seed that had no business here, might be brought in from Saskatchewan in the turn-ups, and nature reprehensibly tampered with. They need Ruskin's reminder that the actual flower is the plant's

Ethusa Cynapium.

FOOL'S PARSLEY
Engraving from *Flora Londinensis*

highest fulfilment, and a reminder that flowers are not here exclusively for herbaria and county floras and plant geography. They are here first of all for delight.

There is something else, too, we need, and which botanists whose view goes beyond distribution and classification can provide, a guide to plants in Britain better than the numberless small flower books and better than Bentham and Hooker's *Handbook of the British Flora*, or Hooker's *Students' Flora of the British Isles*, which, revised again and again, has been the leader since 1870. Both books are well behind the present width of knowledge about plants in Britain, and all the changes in botanical understanding, and they are dry, as though the world of plants were a dry, brown herbarium.

Fifteen years ago plans were announced for a *Biological Flora of Great Britain*. It would describe each species, its range in space and time, its

47

relation to soil and to climate and the other plants that it lives among, the way it reproduces itself, how it gets pollinated, how its seeds are dispersed, its physiology, and parasites, and so on. In spite of the war—and actually on the ground that if the war is a bad time for original research, it is a better time for arranging accumulated facts—the first parts of this really scientific flora are now at last being published. We want also a popular guide planned in the same way, a guide as nearly as possible complete, which enables us to distinguish common, and rare, and alien, to know something of the history of the British flora, and something of the underlying problems of the existence of plants ; a book written by an expert who is not emotionally dead to all excellence in plants, and not above realising that to popularise is one of the points of having scientific method and research.

YELLOW STONECROP
Engraving from *Flora Londinensis*, 1777-1798